THE

SECRET CODE

BOOK

THE SECRET CODE BOOK

BY MICHAEL SHULAN
PICTURES BY DAN REGAN

Watermill Press

Published by Watermill Press, an imprint and registered trademark of Troll Communications L.L.C.

Cover illustration by Dan Regan.

Printed in the United States of America.

10 9 8 7 6 5 4 3 2 1

TABLE OF CONTENTS

INTRODUCTION

When you want to send a secret message, one of the best ways to do it is to use a code. With a code, you can hide the real meaning of a message from people who aren't supposed to know it. And, you can have a lot of fun doing it.

There are hundreds of different codes. Some of them are very old. Some are quite famous because they played a big part in history. But just because a code is old doesn't mean that it won't work for you. You can use these ancient codes today. They will be as secret as ever.

Some codes mix up the letters of the alphabet, or use numbers instead. Others use flashes of light or sounds. Some unusual codes even use strange signals or marks that you can make up yourself. This book will show you how to do all of these code techniques, and a few more, too. There are also codes to decode. You will find the answers on page 48, but do your own decoding before you check the answers. They contain secret messages especially for you!

So, take this book to some safe place, where nobody is looking over your shoulder. Then open it up and begin.

ATTACK

LYSANDER'S CODE

In ancient Greece, generals had a hard time keeping their messages secret. Important letters were usually sent by runners—men trained to run long distances, who knew how to slip by the enemy. Even so, at times they were caught, and the messages fell into enemy hands.

Lysander, a Spartan general, invented one of the first known codes. Sparta was at war with Athens, another Greek state. Persia, a nearby country, fought on Sparta's side. But Lysander suspected that Persia was planning to change sides and attack Sparta. In order to save Sparta, he needed information and he needed to act very soon.

When a runner arrived in the military camp with a letter, Lysander took the letter, and also asked for the runner's belt. You see, it wasn't the letter that was important. The letter was a trick, planned by Lysander and the runner. It was actually the belt that held the secret message!

Alphabet letters were written inside the belt. But, for safety, they were all scrambled up and impossible to read. Lysander knew what to do. He took out his baton—a wooden stick like a small bat that Greek generals carried. He wound the belt around the baton. Like magic, the letters lined up and spelled out a message.

The Persians were planning to attack! Lysander had what he needed to know. The Spartans attacked first and won the war. Sparta was saved by a coded message!

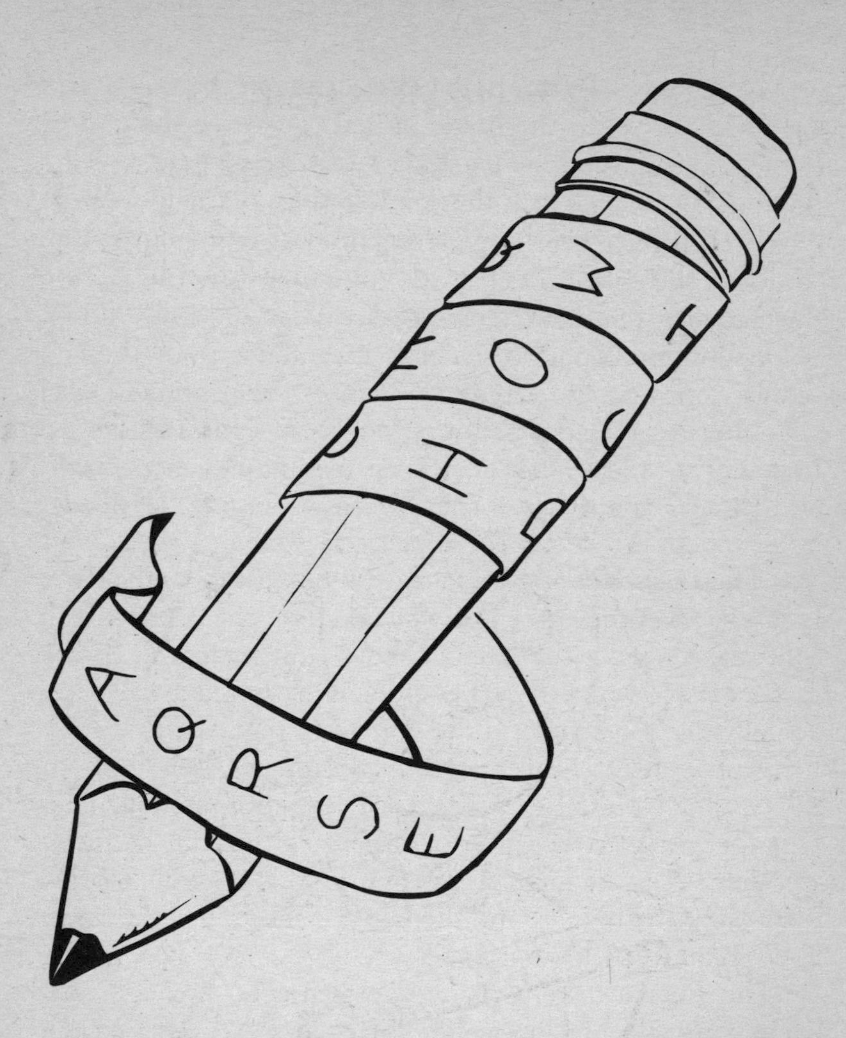

Here is how you can send secret messages to a friend using Lysander's code. To do it, you need two pencils of the same thickness, and a long, thin strip of paper.

Using a small piece of scotch tape, attach one end of the strip of paper near the eraser. Turn the pencil slowly with one hand and guide the paper down and around the entire pencil with the other. Put a small piece of scotch tape on the end to hold it in place.

Write a message on the paper, starting at the eraser end and moving toward the point. When you reach the end of the paper strip, turn the pencil and start a new line.

When you unwind the paper, the message will be jumbled and impossible to read. The only one who will be able to understand it will be your friend—when he or she rewinds the strip of paper around the pencil just like yours.

CAESAR'S CODE

Julius Caesar, one of the greatest Roman emperors, invented another kind of simple code. When he wanted to send a secret message, he would make it difficult to understand by shifting the letters of the alphabet. Here is how he did it.

First, Caesar wrote down all the letters of the alphabet in a line.

A B C D E F G H I J K L M N O P Q R S T U V W X Y Z

Then he replaced each letter of his message with the letter of the alphabet three places farther down the line.

In Caesar's code A=D, because D is the third letter following A. With practice, you will be able to figure this out quickly, but at the beginning it's a good idea to count the spaces out on the alphabet line with your finger. B=E, C=F, D=G, and so on. At the end of the alphabet, you will run out of letters for X, Y, and Z. Go back to the beginning of the alphabet and finish counting there. Then X=A, Y=B, and Z=C.

SEND TROOPS in Caesar's code would be VHQG WURRSV.

Using Caesar's code, you can skip down as many letters of the alphabet as you want, as long as you keep it the same for the whole message. Remember, whenever you run out of spaces at the end of the alphabet, go back to the beginning. Decoding a message in Caesar's code is as easy as coding one. Just count back on the alphabet line for each letter of the message.

Now that you understand the way Caesar's code works, use strips of alphabet letters, and let them do your counting for you. Cut out the alphabet strips on page 15. They will make coding far easier.

The short strip, A through Z, is your letter code, and the longer strip A through Z and A through Z again—a double alphabet—is your coding alphabet.

Place the letter code (short strip) over the coding alphabet (long strip). Line up the A on the short strip with whatever code letter you choose, if you want to send a code. All the letters of your letter code will automatically be right above their correct code letters. Because you have a double alphabet to use for coding (or decoding), you can slide your A through Z letter code to the right or left and still not run out of code letters.

When the instructions tell you to skip down (to the right) 4 places on the alphabet line, position the A of your letter code over the letter E on your coding alphabet. And, when the instructions are to count back (to the left) 4 places, position the A over the letter W on the coding alphabet.

Here is a message to decode in Caesar's code. Every letter of the alphabet has been moved down 6 spaces.

SKKZ SK OT ZNK CUUJY!

There is a problem with Caesar's code. It is too easy for someone else to figure out. For one thing, the words in code still have the same number of letters as in the original message. So, to make this code more difficult, write out the coded message in groups of three letters. If the message does not divide up evenly, add one or two extra letters at the end. It doesn't matter what they are. When the message is decoded, it will be clear that they do not count.

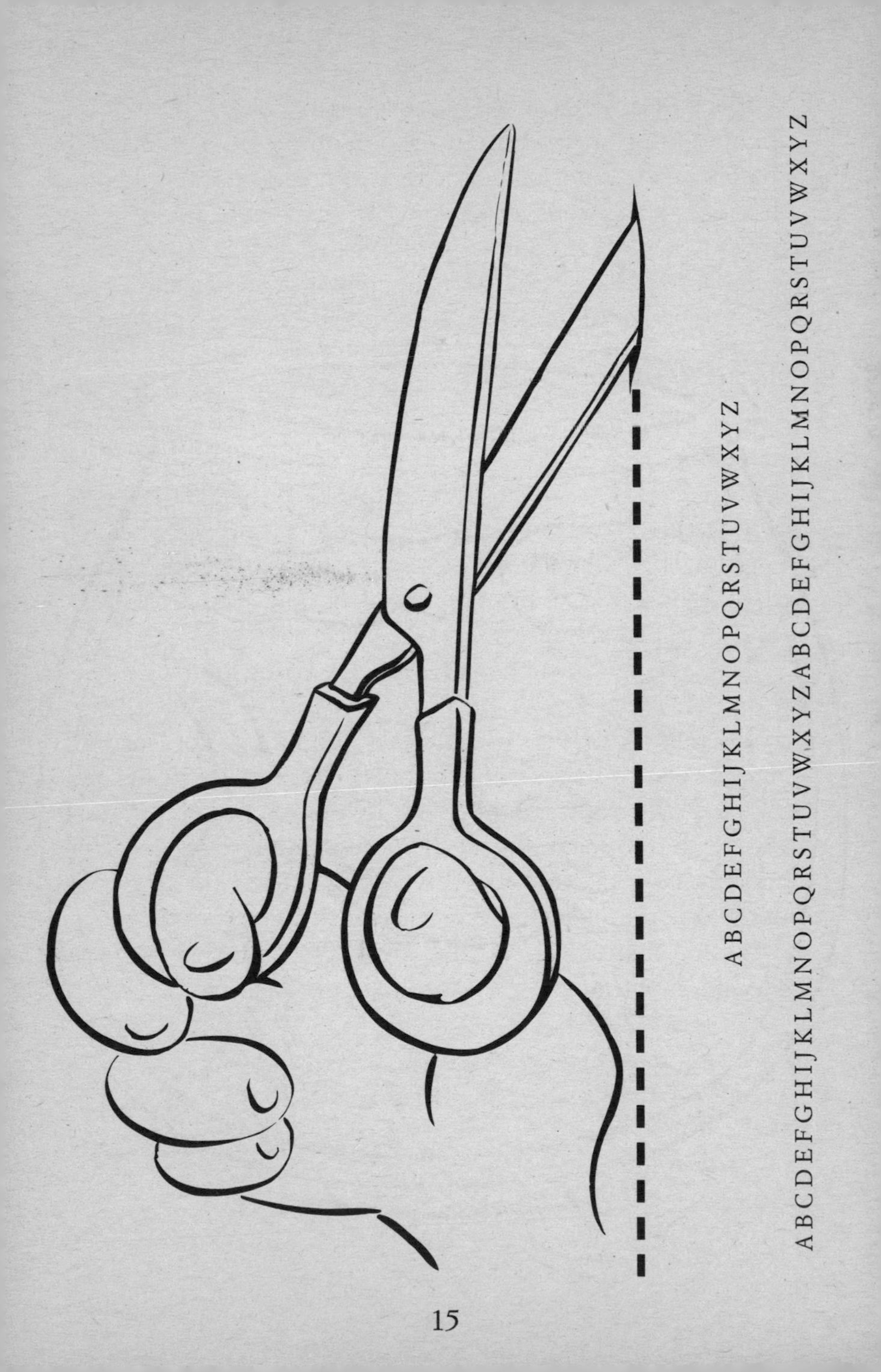
A B C D E F G H I J K L M N O P Q R S T U V W X Y Z
A B C D E F G H I J K L M N O P Q R S T U V W X Y Z A B C D E F G H I J K L M N O P Q R S T U V W X Y Z

KVL IHK WWD
HWQ RGC!

This message is in Caesar's code, skipping down 4 places in the alphabet.

WSQ ISR ILE WWI IRC SYB!

One easy way to put a message in code is to spell it backwards. Divide the message up into groups of three letters just as you did before.

CHECK YOUR SHOES in code is then SEO HSR UOY KCE HCZ. But, once again, this code is very easy to figure out. So, why not spell your message backwards, and then put it into Caesar's code:

DON'T EAT THE FISH	—	the plain message
HSI FEH TTA ETN ODZ	—	backwards, with one extra letter
KVL IHK WWD HWQ RGC	—	Caesar's code, moving each letter 3 places down on the alphabet line

Here is a message to decode. It is done the same way as the example. Remember, first count back three spaces in the alphabet for each letter. Then turn the whole line around.

HPW VXU WAC.

MONK'S CODE

The best codes always make a message difficult to understand. Simple codes can be used quickly and easily. They work well, but for extra-secret messages, they often are not safe enough. Codes that are really safe almost always take more time to prepare and use. But they are usually worth the extra effort.

One of the safest codes of all was invented by a German monk over 450 years ago. The idea is very simple, and the code works as well now as it did then. To use the Monk's code, you need two code books, one for yourself and one for a friend. Any notebook will do but a small code book is easier to slip into your pocket, or to hide when you're not using it.

Here is how the Monk's code works. Every letter of the alphabet has its own page in the code book. Each letter has a list of words and simple phrases—one or two words that go together. For example, here are some sample lists:

A	B	C	D
night	it is	when	about it
beautiful	tomorrow	will you	onions
cold soup	you are	at school	please
right	give me	tree	thank you

You need a code book with 26 lists like these to put a message into Monk's code. For each letter of the message you pick a word or phrase from that letter's list. Pick words from the list that fit together, so that the message written out in code will read like an ordinary letter.

For example, here is how the word BAD could be written out in Monk's code, using the sample lists:

Give me cold soup, please.
or
It is beautiful. Thank you.
or
You are right about it.

Every code has its weakness. The weakness of Monk's code is that the messages are quite long. But, the code is one of the safest there is, since only people who have code books can understand the message. The longer your lists are for each letter of the alphabet, the better your code will be. Make sure not to repeat any of the words, though. And, always be sure that you keep your code book in a safe place.

You get an "beautiful"!

PIG-PEN

During the American Civil War, Northern prisoners in Southern jails used a strange looking code to send secret messages to their friends. To understand Pig-Pen, first draw the lines for a tic-tac-toe game. Next, write the alphabet in the tic-tac-toe spaces this way:

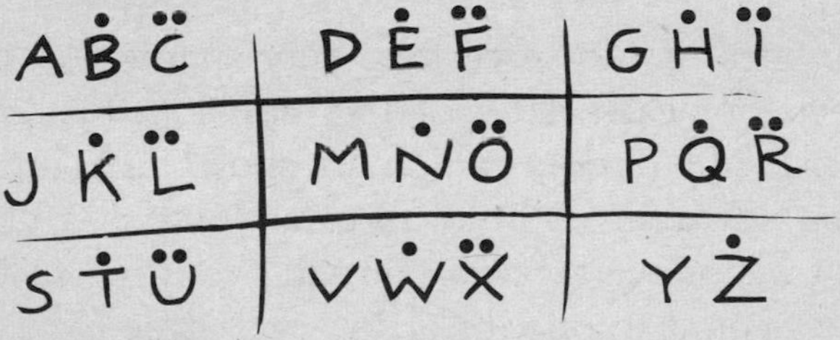

A Ḃ C̈	D Ė F̈	G Ḣ Ï
J K̇ L̈	M Ṅ Ö	P Q̇ R̈
S Ṫ Ü	V Ẇ Ẍ	Y Ż

Here is how to put a message into code. First, draw each letter of the alphabet using the pattern of lines around it in the Pig-Pen key. For example, A= ⌋, and M= ☐. But, there are three letters in every section of the pattern (except for the very last one, where there are only two). In order to show the differences between letters in a group, the second letter of each group in the pattern has a dot on top of it. The third letter in each group has two dots. So, for the second letter, draw the pattern and put a dot in it. B= ·⌋. For the third letter, draw the pattern and put two dots in it. O= ⊡. And for the first letter, do not use any dots.

So, in Pig-Pen code, BE CAREFUL=

Here is a message for you to decode:

!

MORSE CODE

Morse code was invented to send messages by telegraph. You can use it in many different ways. At night, you can blink it out with a flashlight. You can beat out your message on a drum, or with a stick on a rock. You can even whistle it, or flash it with a mirror in the daytime, using the light of the sun.

The idea of Morse code is very simple. All it is, is an alphabet. For each letter of the alphabet, this code has a signal made up of dots (which are short) and dashes (which are long). A dash is three times as long as a dot. That is always true, no matter how you send your message. An easy way is to count to one for a dot, and three for a dash. For example: A=· — N=— ·
1 123 123 1

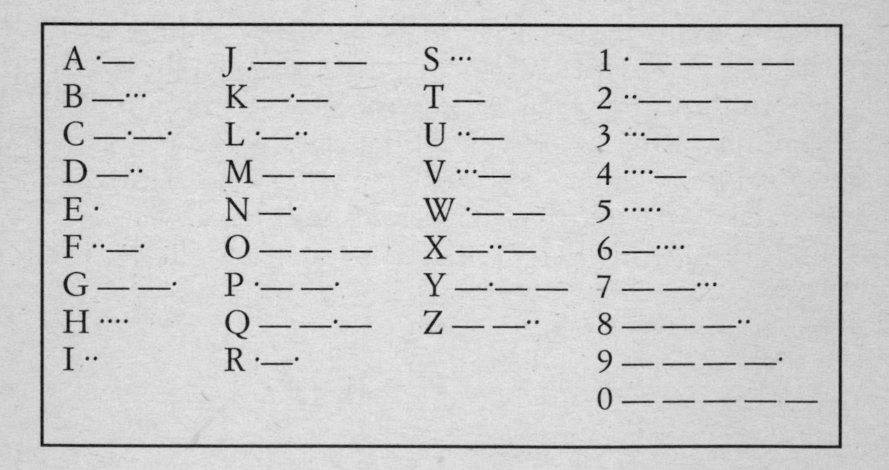

A ·—	J .———	S ···	1 ·————
B —···	K —·—	T —	2 ··———
C —·—·	L ·—··	U ··—	3 ···——
D —··	M ——	V ···—	4 ····—
E ·	N —·	W ·——	5 ·····
F ··—·	O ———	X —··—	6 —····
G ——·	P ·——·	Y —·——	7 ——···
H ····	Q ——·—	Z ——··	8 ———··
I ··	R ·—·		9 ————·
			0 —————

Here is a Morse code question for you:

—·—· ·— —· —·—— ——— ··— —·— · ·
·——· ·— ··· · —·—· ·—· · — ?

The main problem with using the Morse code is that too many people know it. This means that your signals may be understood. The most important thing to do, then, is to make sure that nobody is around when you send your message. But, it is also a very good idea to put your message into another code before you send it in Morse. Any code written out in letters will do.

For instance, combining Caesar's code (skipping three letters down the alphabet line), with the number codes in Morse, try this one:

·—— —·— ····
—·· ——·— ···— ——·· ···· ··—
·—·· ···— —··· ···· ···—

SQUARE CODE

One of the most successful codes used in World War II was the Square code. It was invented especially for use with Morse code. Every word in Square code is made up of the letters, A, E, I, N, and T. These are the shortest letters in Morse code. So, if you put a message into Square code, then sending it in Morse code will be very easy. But Square code is also a very good code to use alone.

The code is called Square code because all the letters of the alphabet are written out in a square. There are five rows of letters, with five letters in each one. The letter J is never used: any J in a message becomes an I in code. Along the top and side of the square, the letters A, E, I, N, and T are also written out. Here is a sample key:

	A	E	I	N	T
A	E	S	C	X	L
E	W	Z	H	T	G
I	D	M	V	Q	A
N	R	U	K	Y	O
T	I	N	B	P	F

The letters inside the square should be jumbled. Write the key down in your code book. If you change the order of the letters, the whole code changes, too. So, be careful when you copy a code.

To put a message into Square code is simple. Find each letter inside the square. With your finger, first trace up the row until you reach the letter on top, above the line. Write this letter down. For example, take the letter U. Tracing it up, the letter on top is E. Next, go back to the original letter again. This time, trace it across to the left until you reach the letter the farthest to the side, the one outside the line. For U, this letter is N. The code for U, then, is EN. Every letter of a message is made up of two letters in Square code. Always put the letter from the top A, E, I, N, T line first.

Using the sample square, the message LOOK OUT becomes

TA TN TN IN TN EN NE!

Every letter of the original message is made up of two letters in code. And, all the letters of the coded message are made up of A, E, I, N, and T.

To decode a message, trace the outside letters back into the square to the point where the two imaginary lines cross. EI in code, for example, is M. An imaginary line down from the top line, and another imaginary line across from the side, cross at M.

AI AT AI NN TN EN
TE AA NE AT NE?

NUMBER CODE

Instead of writing out your secret messages in letters, you can put them in code using numbers instead. In this sort of code, every letter of the alphabet has a number from 1 to 26. But, if you make A=1, B=2, C=3, and so on—in order—all the way up to Z=26, then your code will be much too easy to figure out. A better way is to give each letter a number in no particular order. Write down all the letters in your code book, and then choose a number for each letter. The list in your code book is called a key. When it comes time to put a message into code or to decode it, you work from your key.

A=11	G= 1	M=19	S =16	Y=23
B=25	H=26	N=13	T = 9	Z=17
C= 4	I =12	O= 7	U = 2	
D=24	J = 5	P =14	V= 5	
E=21	K=22	Q=20	W= 8	
F =18	L = 3	R =10	X =15	

22-21-21-14 9-26-21 22-21-23 12-13 11 16-11-18-21 14-3-11-4-21!

There is another number code which does not need a code book key. The trick to this code is that it uses a key word which you pick out yourself. You can use any word, as long as none of the letters in it are repeated. To work with this code, write out the letters of the key word first. Then list the rest of the alphabet in order. But, skip the letters you have already written down from the key word. Then write out the numbers from 1 to 26 in order, under your list of letters.

Using the key word DANGER, your code list would look like this:

D	A	N	G	E	R	B	C	F	H	I	J	K
1	2	3	4	5	6	7	8	9	10	11	12	13

L	M	O	P	Q	S	T	U	V	W	X	Y	Z
14	15	16	17	18	19	20	21	22	23	24	25	26

Here is a message written out in the DANGER code:

1 2 3 4 5 6! 15 5 5 20 15 5
20 16 15 16 6 6 16 23.

The advantage to this code is that you don't need to keep a permanent code book. If you remember the key word, it is simple to make out a list when it is time to code or decode a letter. It is not quite as safe as the first number code, but if you change the key word often, it will be very difficult for someone to figure out your messages.

NUMBER—SQUARE CODE

Another kind of square code uses numbers. Make three separate boxes for the alphabet. Each box should be divided with a tic-tac-toe pattern. Since there are three boxes with 9 spaces each, you will have 27 spaces—just enough for the whole alphabet with one square left over.

①	1	2	3
1	A	B	C
2	D	E	F
3	G	H	I

②	1	2	3
1	J	K	L
2	M	N	O
3	P	Q	R

③	1	2	3
1	S	T	U
2	V	W	X
3	Y	Z	

When the boxes are made up, the messages are easy to spell out in numbers. Take a real message SEE ME LATER. The letter S is in the third box, so it has a key number right away, 3 for the third box. Its position is in the first line down, so it gets a second number, 1. It is in the first row so it gets another 1. S is 311. E is naturally 122. 1 for the first box, 2 for the second line, and 2 for the second row. The word SEE is 311, 122, 122. ME is 212, 122. The complete message is:

311, 122, 122   212, 122   231, 111, 321, 122, 233.

Try this message:
133   322, 133, 231, 231   121, 122   321, 123, 122, 233, 122.

SLOT CODE

Confusing messages can be terribly difficult for anyone else but those in the know to figure out.

For a real puzzler—in case your message is intercepted—use the Slot code. In Slot code you will need to use pieces of paper of exactly the same size. Cut slots, or "windows," into two sheets of paper. They are your keys. When either you or your friend want to send a message, first place the key on top of another sheet of paper, and write the real secret message in the window of your key. Then cover the rest of the bottom sheet with other messages. You can be funny, or mysterious, or even make up nonsense words to further confuse anyone who might come across your message sheet. But be sure to have a couple of genuine messages, too.

Both you and your friend must have exactly the same slotted sheets of paper. Be sure you know which way is up on your key sheet, and which side is the front. Mark your key with an arrow.

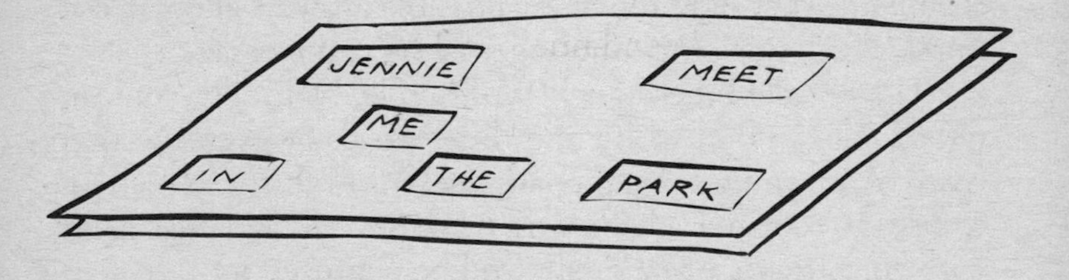

Anyone who happens to find your message will know it is a code, but they will not be able to read it without a key. They will have all the messages—but won't know which one is the real message.

FOURTH WORD CODE

Another word message code which is puzzling to other people is the Fourth Word code. Use this code when you and your friend want an easy but safe code.

In the Fourth Word code you write four different messages. You might write:

"Not tonight Sally let's" "now is watches get"
"later good us together"

Each group of words won't make sense, but reading a message from every first word, second word, third word, and fourth word does make sense. Because you and your friend have agreed upon a Fourth Word code, your friend instantly understands your message: "Let's get together." But the code is difficult for other people to figure out. Even when they crack the code, they come up with four different possible answers, such as "Not now later," or "Tonight is good," or "Sally watches us," *and* the correct code "Let's get together." They have too many possible answers and will not know which one of the messages is the real message.

This is called the Fourth Word code. Naturally, you can choose the second word, the third word, or even the first word. And, you can keep changing—from third, to second, to first, to fourth. Only be sure to keep your signals straight with your friend, or he or she will be confused too!

SUPER SIMPLE CODE

You will always need a super simple, quick and easy code. Since many codes are blocked out in three letter or four letter words, you can take advantage of this fact to give a would-be code breaker double trouble. They will think you are using a difficult code, but you are really using a very simple one.

What you do is this. Spell out your code in three letter words which look like a complex code. But your code is only the middle letter of each word. Use any other letters for the beginning and ending letters. I LEAVE TONIGHT can be written:

tix nlo ber maw ivy kee ltm poq inr zia hgo lhv rtw,

or

tib plm sev lam svl pep vtb qot pnp bic jgk mhn stb.

> Try this one:
>
> pet pab lst vym tab cst opi pit set!

SHOPPING LIST CODE

A way to keep a code really secret is to make up a fake shopping list. Who would suspect that Tomatoes—$1.05, Lettuce—89¢, and Radishes—29¢, penciled on a slip of paper, would mean YES? But it would, if you used a Shopping List code and decided that Y=5, E=89, and S=29.

To make a Shopping List code, first write out an alphabet. Assign numbers, 1 through 99, to each letter. For instance:

A= 2
B=16
C=43
D=11
E=89
F=19
G=45
H=18
I = 8
J =39
K= 7
L=98
M=33
N=46
O=69
P=12
Q=55
R=73
S =29
T=75
U=52
V =21
W=99
X =27
Y = 5
Z = 3

To use it, make up a list of groceries and jot down the prices. The prices will carry your code messages. Use dollar amounts if you want to, but since only the cent amounts are part of your code, you can ignore the numbers to the left of decimals.

If you want to send someone the message DON'T LEAVE, write it out this way:

Hamburger	$ 3.11
Potato Chips	.69
Ketchup	.46
Rolls	.75
Cans of Chili	.98
Apples	.89
Dog Food	1.02
Pineapple	1.21
Cheese	.89

The Shopping List code is very much like the Number code, but there is an important difference. If a Number code message were intercepted, anyone picking it up would know it was a code. Anyone finding a Shopping List code message would simply think, "Hmm, a shopping list" and never give it another thought. You can disguise a message cleverly by quickly writing a list of the groceries, or snacks, you "bought!"

Here is a list of snacks for you:	
Apple juice	$ .43
Nuts	2.18
Raisins	.89
Apricots	.89
Oranges	.73
Brownies	1.29

LETTER CODE

You want to send a message, "Meet me at three tomorrow," and you want to keep it quiet. You hide this fact in an ordinary looking note. You "bury" the words. Here is how it can be done.

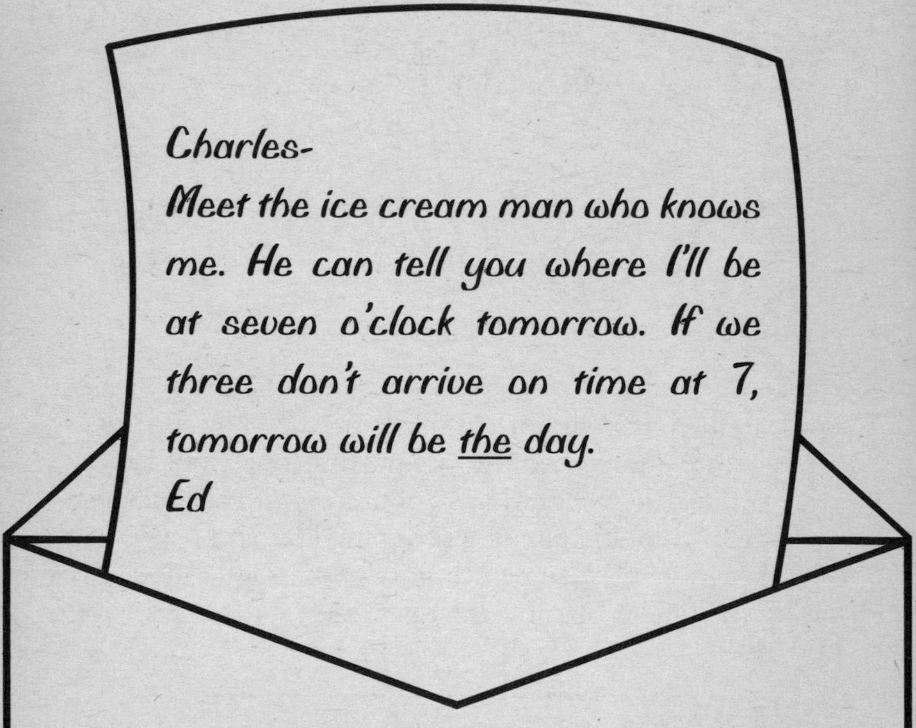

Charles-
Meet the ice cream man who knows
me. He can tell you where I'll be
at seven o'clock tomorrow. If we
three don't arrive on time at 7,
tomorrow will be the day.
Ed

Where is the code message? What is the code? Read the first words of each line, and read down: "Meet me at three tomorrow." Writing fake letters can often put other people on the wrong track.

Here is a message just for you:
This is your last chance and it is also your only chance to win a spectacular club prize! So be quick and come to the clubhouse at one for the drawing. Hurry!

SEMAPHORE CODE

There are other ways to signal besides using Morse code. One of the well-known signal codes is Semaphore. The word means *sign bearing*, and semaphore is basically a body language. The idea is to use your arms to spell out letters. Each alphabet letter is an arm code. Look at the illustrations for cues on how to signal each letter.

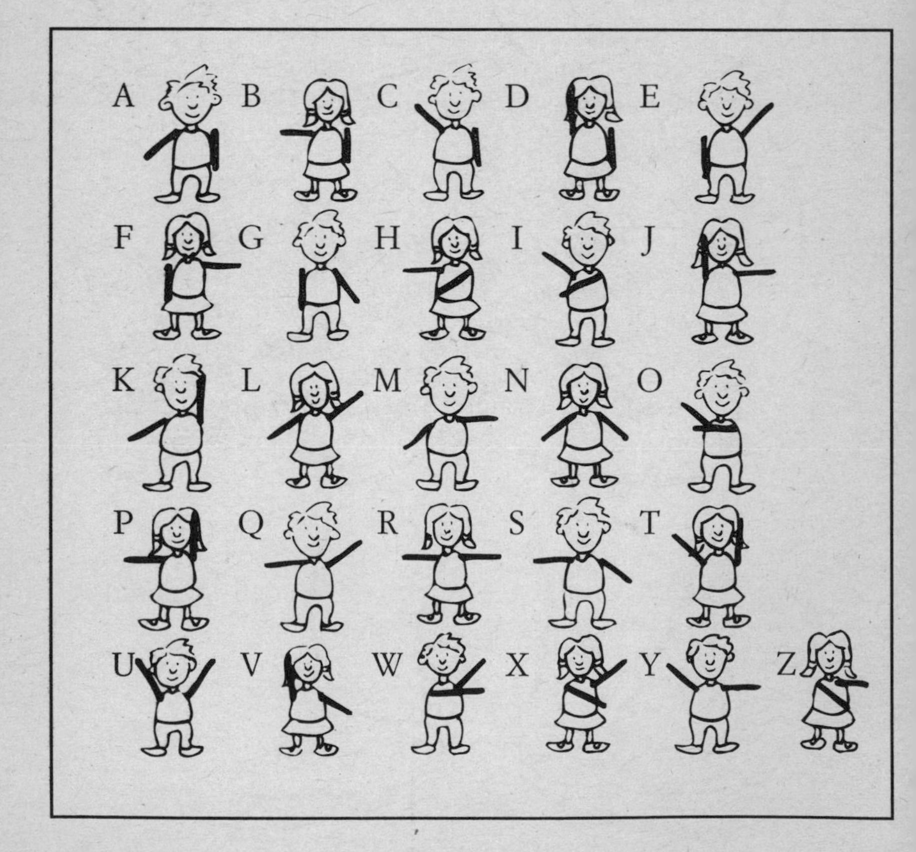

Other important semaphore signals are made by waving your arms when you are ready to send a message.

And crossing your arms above your head to signal a mistake. If the semaphore sender crosses arms overhead, it means cancel the letter message, and word. If the receiver crosses arms overhead, it means the message isn't coming across and the sender must go back and start the word all over again. It also may mean not ready.

The receiver's ready signal is a left arm raised.

Arms held straight out signal the end of a word.

And, arms held straight down followed by arms extended means that the message is complete.

Just like the Morse code, Semaphore codes require practice. Their signals don't leave a shred of evidence, but remember, you can't afford to be seen either, or people will know you are sending codes. Of course, since not many people know semaphore, your messages will be private ones, at least for awhile!

Semaphores are really quite useful. You can signal by Semaphore when you are within sight of your friend but don't want to make a sound or when you are too far away to talk. It's fun to use flags, too. With flags, you can be seen farther away. Tack colorful triangles of material or paper to sticks or poles, and start sending messages!

Try this Semaphore code message:

KEY WORD CODE

Key word codes need a code book first, and second, your own personal code that you make up and share with a friend. The way a Key Word code works is this:

You may decide that gorilla means "ice cream parlor," ketchup means "meet me," oranges means "tomorrow," and smile, "after school." And, of course, your list has many more words. They will be your key words, and handy for you to use.

In the Key Word code above KETCHUP GORILLA SMILE ORANGES would mean "Meet me (at) the ice cream parlor after school tomorrow."

In Key Word codes you choose your words, your code answers, and, of course your list can grow and grow. You can drop codes that aren't useful. And, you can keep adding on ones that are.

If, for instance:

TEPEE="that is"
PRAIRIE="those are"
STIRRUP="can't see you"
UNDER="of"
BICYCLE="Saturday"
RUNNING="you"

SADDLE="this is"
BIT="see you"
HOCKEY="he"
ABOVE="from"
BECAUSE="for"
GLIDING="at home"
TENNIS="she"

SADDLE BECAUSE RUNNING

is a code just for you!

INVISIBLE INK

Invisible ink is another good way to keep your messages secret. It's not really a code, but you can use it for secret writing. You can write anything you want in invisible ink, and when you are finished, the message will look just like a sheet of blank paper. And, to be extra safe, you can put your messages into code first. Being in code *and* written in invisible ink, your messages should be impossible for anyone else to figure out!

There are many different liquids you can use for ink, but two of the best are lemon juice and milk because you can find both of them around the house. To write your message, use the wrong end of a wooden match, a pen that is all dried up, or anything else that has a point. Dip it in the lemon juice or milk, and write out your message in clear letters. If you print, it will probably be easier to read when you make the writing appear again. Don't use too much ink, because if you wet the paper through, when it dries it will be wrinkled. This could alert other people to the fact that there is a secret message written on your sheet of paper.

The message will show up only when the piece of paper is heated. Hold it over a hot light bulb and the writing will show up clearly in a few moments, in brown.

If you want to make your secret message even harder for someone else to detect, don't use a blank piece of paper. Instead, write with invisible ink between the lines of a letter. Write with lemon juice or milk in the empty spaces, or even over the other writing if you want. The letter will serve as a decoy, and nobody will suspect there is a secret message hidden in it.

SECRET PLACES

As you learn more and more codes, your code book is bound to grow. It is fun to have a book with all of your secrets in it—a book you have written yourself! You might even decide to put the keys to your codes in your diary, or even write your diary itself in code.

But remember: the most important thing about a code is that it is a secret. A code book explains everything, and anyone who finds it can decode all of your messages. This means that you must be extra careful to keep it in a safe place. The safest place of all, of course, is inside your head. You should only write down what is impossible to remember.

If you know that someone has found your code book, then you know it is time to change your codes. Or, you can even send out false messages in the code that has been "broken" to fool the person who has done it.

The best places to hide your code book are the unexpected ones. It is fun to hide your code book and think up better and better places—the ones no one will ever think of. You could find an old book. Cut a square hole in its middle and slip your code book inside. Or, think of the space at the back of your desk drawer. Pull the drawer out and place your code book in hiding. It is also easy to tape a folder under a table and keep your code book in it. A place most searchers would overlook is inside a waste paper basket, especially if there are some old crumpled up papers in it too. Scotch tape your code book to the bottom. If your code is on a piece of paper, roll it up in a window shade. In a super emergency, mail your code book to yourself. No one can peek at it while it is in the mail. A small code book can easily fit inside an old shoe, where very few people would ever search. Or, if you have an old coat or windbreaker hanging in your closet, slip the code book in a pocket. The important thing—*always*—is to keep your code book where you and only you can find it, and where no one else would suspect it could be.

BREAKING CODES

Breaking a coded message—decoding it without the key or knowing what kind of a code was used—is not easy. The purpose of a code, after all, is to keep a message secret, and the better a code is, the harder it will be to break. The method itself is not difficult. But, you have to be patient. Here is what to do to solve most letter and word codes.

The first methods to try are the simple ones. Spell the whole message backwards and see if it makes sense that way. If not, try spelling each word backwards, but keep the order of words the same.

If the code is in numbers, see if it is a simple case of numbering the letters of the alphabet in order from 1 to 26—A=1, B=2, and so on.

Probably none of these methods is going to work. Why? Knowing as much about codes as you do now, you ought to know why. These codes are too easy. Would you use a code like this yourself? You shouldn't. But maybe someone else will, and you will be lucky.

If the simple methods do not unlock codes, the hard work begins. To break a good code, you need to know the following. In English the letter most often used is E. Think of all the words that have an E in them: me, the, tell, see, be, free. There are thousands.

After E, the most common letters are T, A, O, N, R, I, S. If you know this list of letters, then you know the most important thing about breaking codes.

Say you have this message, which you want to break:

PHHW PH ODWHU!

The letter "H' appears in the message 4 times. Because E is the most common letter in English, there is a good chance that the letter "H" in the message stands for E.

```
PHHW  PH  ODWHU!
 EE    E     E
```

The next thing to try is Caesar's code. If "H" is E, how far down the alphabet have all the letters been moved?

A B C D E F G H I J K L M N O P Q R S T U V W X Y Z

If "H" is E, then all the letters have been moved down three spaces. So, count back for each letter of the coded message. And, if you do, the code is broken, and here is what you get:

PHHW PH ODWHU!
MEET ME LATER!

Usually, though, it is not going to be that easy. There may be only one letter E in the message, or none at all. If not, then you have to go through the list of the other common letters T, A, O, N, R, I, S until you find one that works. Pick out a letter in the coded message that appears more than once, if there is one, and try each of the common letters one at a time using the same system you used for the E. If there is no letter in the coded message which appears more than once, then pick one of the letters in a short word to work with.

In this message, "R" is a good letter to work with:
M EQ RSX GSQMRK

If you try making "R" an E, and try a Caesar's code skipping back 13 places, since E is 13 places back from R, it won't work. Neither will Caesar's code making the "R" a T, an A, or an O. But, if you keep trying, you will find that making "R" an N does work. If "R" is an N, then what does this message really mean?

This is the system for breaking some codes. If you have enough patience, it works pretty well. Try different letters of the coded message, and each letter in that important E, T, A, O, N, R, I, S list.

Now here is one final message for you to decode:
AQW JCXG FQPG XGTA YGNN!

ANSWERS

Title	Page	Answer
Caesar's Code	14	Meet me in the woods.
	17	Someone has seen you!
	17	Trust me.
Monk's Code	20	You get an "A."
Pig-Pen	21	Do not be late!
Morse Code	23	Can you keep a secret?
	23	The answer is yes.
Square Code	27	Did you get it?
Number Codes	28	Keep the key in a safe place!
	29	Danger! Meet me tomorrow.
Number—Square Code	30	I will be there.
Super Simple Code	33	Easy as pie!
Shopping List Code	35	Cheers.
Letter Code	37	This is a quick one.
Semaphore Code	40	Don't make a move.
Key Word Code	41	This is for you.
Breaking Codes	47	I am not coming.
	47	You have done very well!